THE

INTERNATIONAL LIBRARY

OF

PIANO MUSIC

ALBUM THIRTEEN

THE
INTERNATIONAL LIBRARY
OF
PIANO MUSIC

Advisory Board

SISTER ALICE MARIE, O.S.U.

LEONARD BERNSTEIN

AARON COPLAND

OLIVER DANIEL

NORMAN DELLO JOIO

ROBERT DUMM

WALTER HENDL

PETER MENNIN

ROBERT PACE

RUDOLF SERKIN

ROGER SESSIONS

HALE SMITH

CLAUDETTE SOREL

Editorial Staff

FELIX GREISSLE
Music Director and Editor-in-Chief

CORINNA MARSH
Literary Editor

ARNOLD BROIDO
Associate Music Editor

ELIZABETH VOLDSTAD
Assistant Music Editor

1968

THE UNIVERSITY SOCIETY, Inc.
Educational Publishers since 1897
New York

© Copyright, 1967, by The University Society, Inc.

All rights reserved.

In addition to its wealth of contemporary material, this *new* INTERNATIONAL LIBRARY OF PIANO MUSIC combines the most successful teaching and playing masterpieces of its predecessors; namely:

Famous Songs and Those Who Made Them	Copyright 1896
The World's Best Music	Copyright 1897
Paderewski — Century Library of Music	Copyright 1900
Modern Music and Musicians	Copyright 1912
La Mejor Musica del Mundo	Copyright 1917
The University Course of Music Study	Copyright 1920
The International Library of Music	Copyright 1925
A Melhor Musica do Mundo	Copyright 1930
The International Library of Music	Copyright 1934
The International Library of Music	Copyright 1945
The International Library of Music	Copyright 1956

Manufactured in the United States of America

TECHNIQUE
(STUDIES AND EXERCISES)

compiled and edited

by

DENES AGAY

TABLE OF CONTENTS
in order of studies

ALBUM THIRTEEN

STUDY NUMBERS

Double Third Scales in All Keys 23
Velocity Studies

      rapid legato figures 1, 7, 10, 20, 28, 29, 30, 32, 36

      rapid broken octave and chords 2, 3, 4, 15, 31, 39

      leggiero 5, 7

      alternation between hands 16, 44, 26

      arpeggios 12, 13

Wrist and Forearm Action 6
Double Notes 9, 11, 14, 21, 22, 23, 24, 25, 26, 27
Solid Chords 8, 27, 33, 37
Octave Studies 16, 17, 27, 33, 34, 40
Polyphony 18, 38

———————
Numerals refer to study numbers

2

Rapid, quiet finger action in wide dynamic range; legatissimo throughout

Johann Baptist Cramer

1

4

Legato broken chords; rapid lateral motion in the right hand

Johann Baptist Cramer

2 Allegro

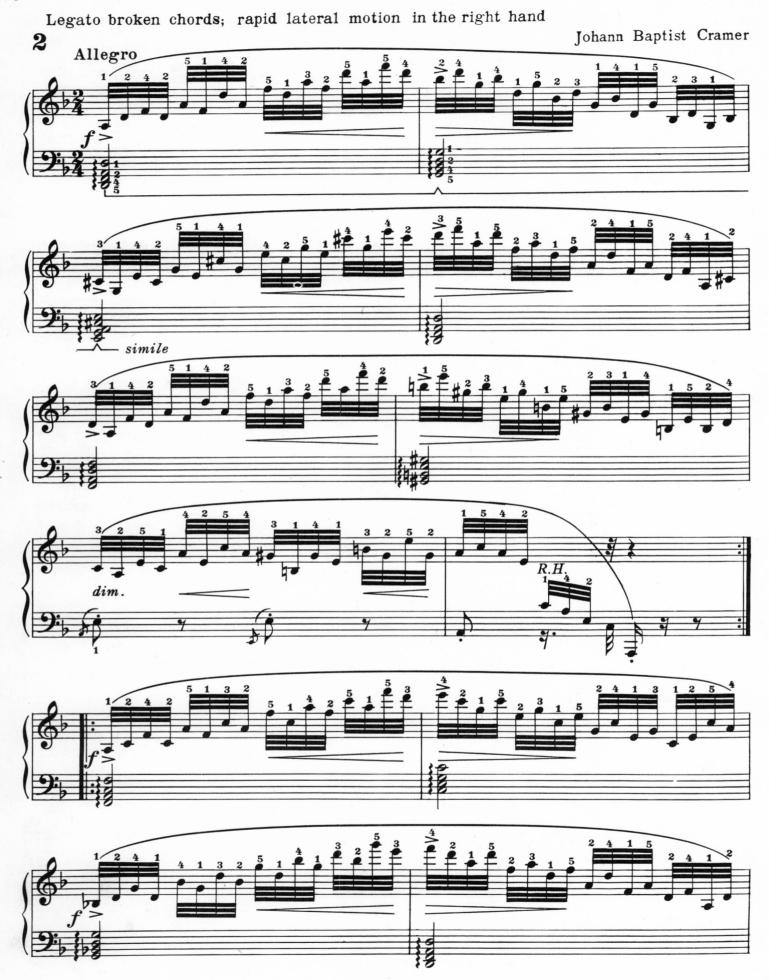

6

Legato broken chords; rapid lateral motion in the left hand

Johann Baptist Cramer

3

8

Broken chords in both hands; parallel and mirror-like contrary motion; firm legato touch

4

Johann Baptist Cramer

Allegro assai

p sempre legato

Velocity scale study; leggiero touch; high speed with utmost evenness is to be attained

Carl Czerny

5

Molto allegro

Swift octave stretches and broken octaves in the left hand; light, loose forearm and wrist action

Carl Czerny

6 Molto allegro

PRELUDE No. 2

Rapid interlacing legato passages in the two hands. Play with utmost evenness.

7

Dmitri Shostakovitch

Allegro

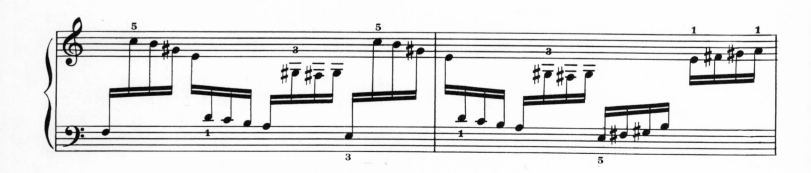

Staccato chords in rapid tempo

Stephen Heller

8 Allegro con brio

Legato double-note figures in the right hand

9

Carl Czerny

Legato figures pivoting around the middle fingers; firm finger action

10

Allegro

Alexander Goedicke

25

Free loose wrist and staccato "lift-off" will help attain speed with clarity.

11

Prestissimo

Johann Baptist Cramer

28

Legato arpeggio study in right hand

Carl Czerny

12

Vivace

Play with a firm touch, keeping joints loose with no stiffness.

13

Carl Czerny

Vivace

36

Study in thirds. Attain speed gradually.

14

Johann Baptist Cramer

Allegro moderato

38

Swift octave stretches

15

Carl Czerny

Staccato octaves alternating between the hands

Carl Czerny

16

ALLA TARANTELLA
Staccato octave passages

Josef Löw

17 Vivace

Polyphony—strive for clarity and accuracy in the leading of voices. Dynamic marks are optional.

George Frederic Händel

SOUVENIR D' ENFANCE

Alternating notes between the two hands. A firm touch, full dynamic range and speed will create a brilliant, virtuoso effect.

Modeste Moussorgsky

Use firm, secure finger action and strong rhythmic pulse.

20

Allegro spiritoso

Johann Baptist Cramer

Rapid double-note figures. Stay relaxed to avoid stiffness and fatigue.

21

Johann Baptist Cramer

Allegro moderato, ma energico

ALLEGRETTO (from Op. 99)

Double note study. Use elastic wrist action.

Robert Schumann

22

Scales in Double Thirds

Play legato at a moderate tempo at first. Increase speed gradually.

23

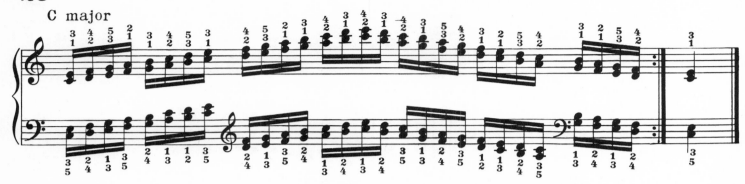

C major

C minor

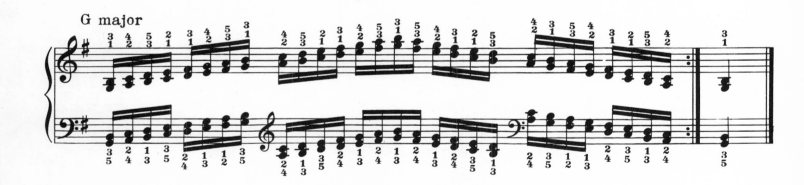

G major

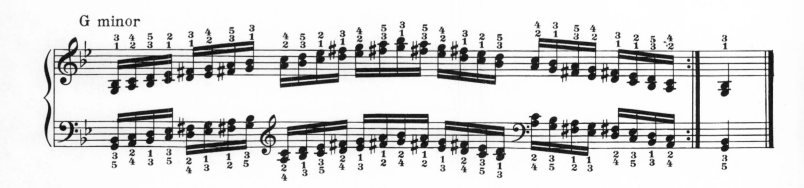

G minor

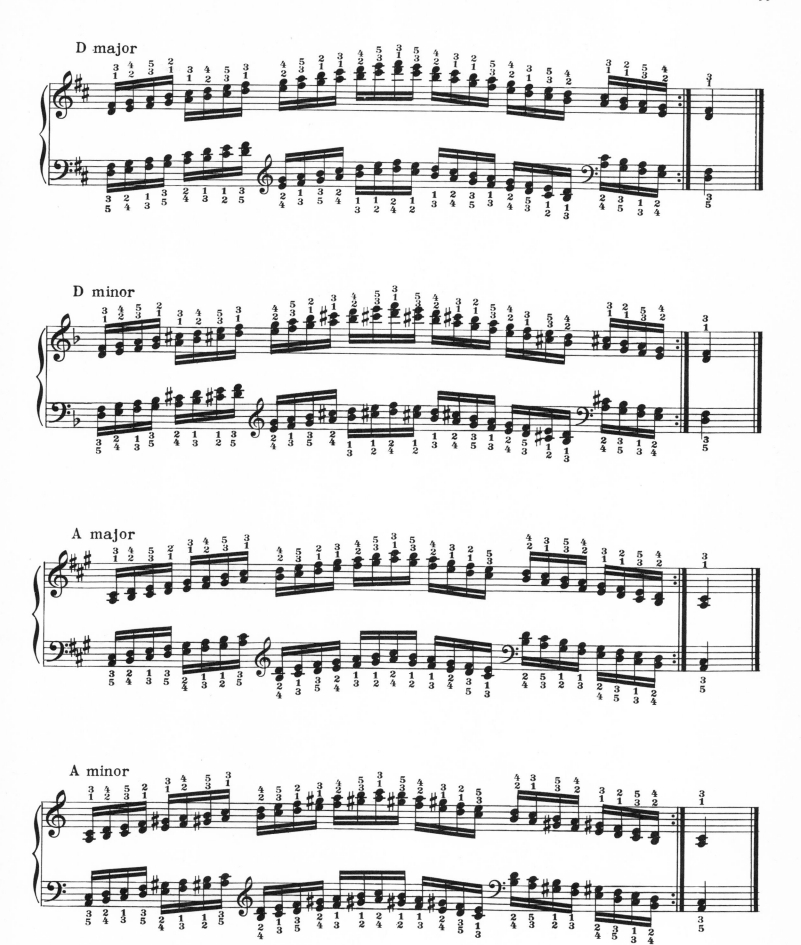

56

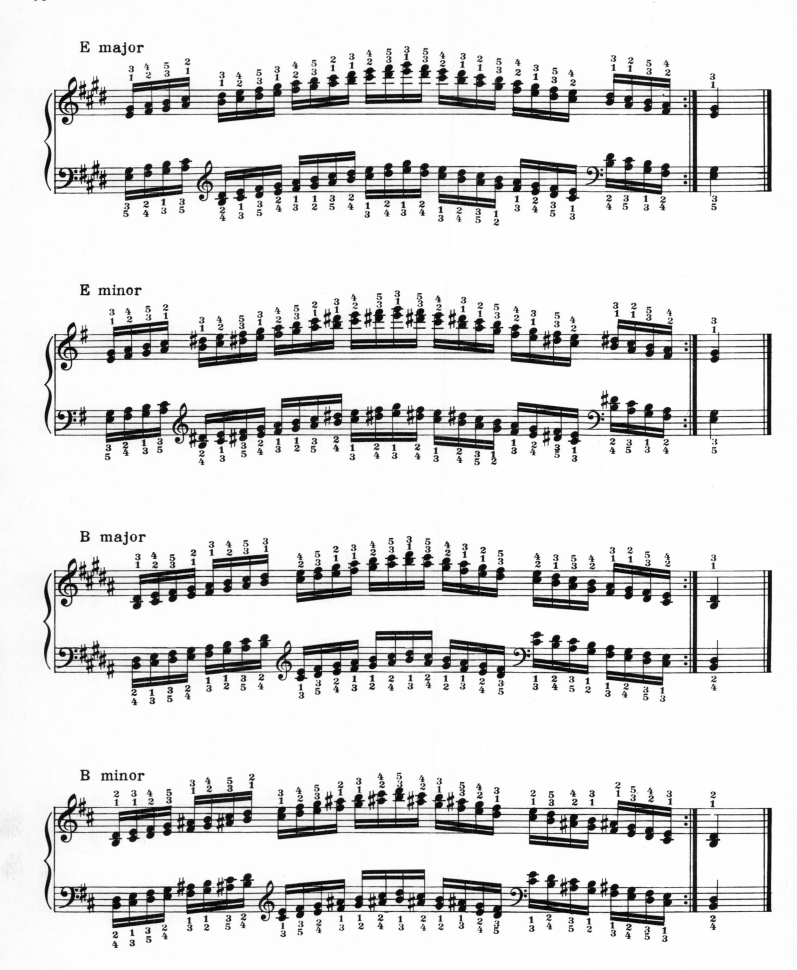

F# major

F# minor

C# major

C# minor

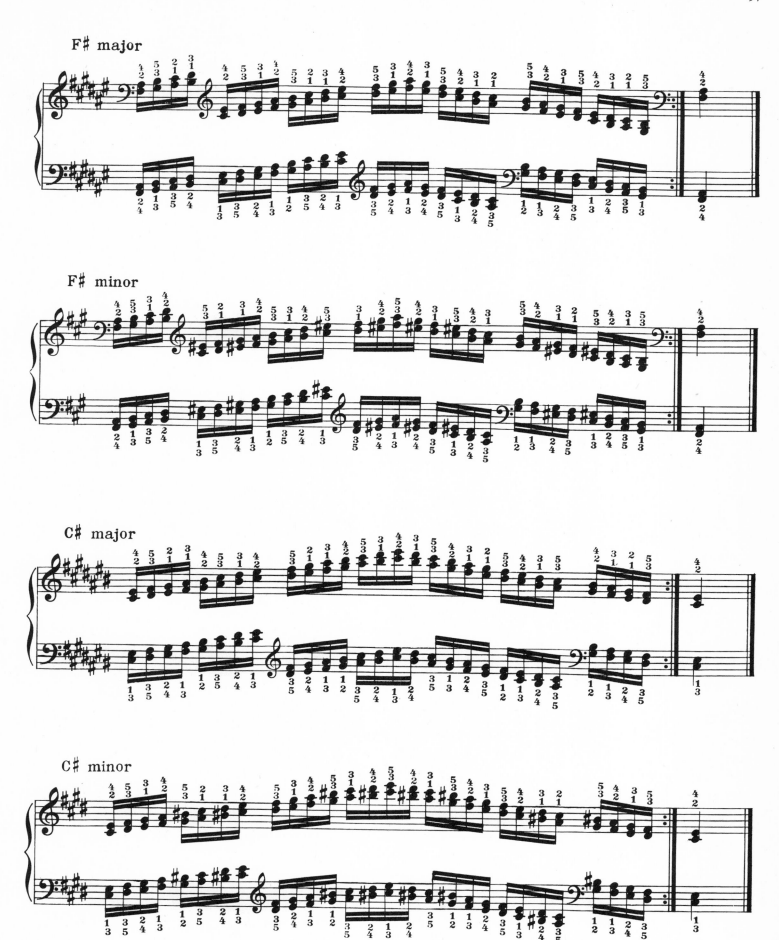

58

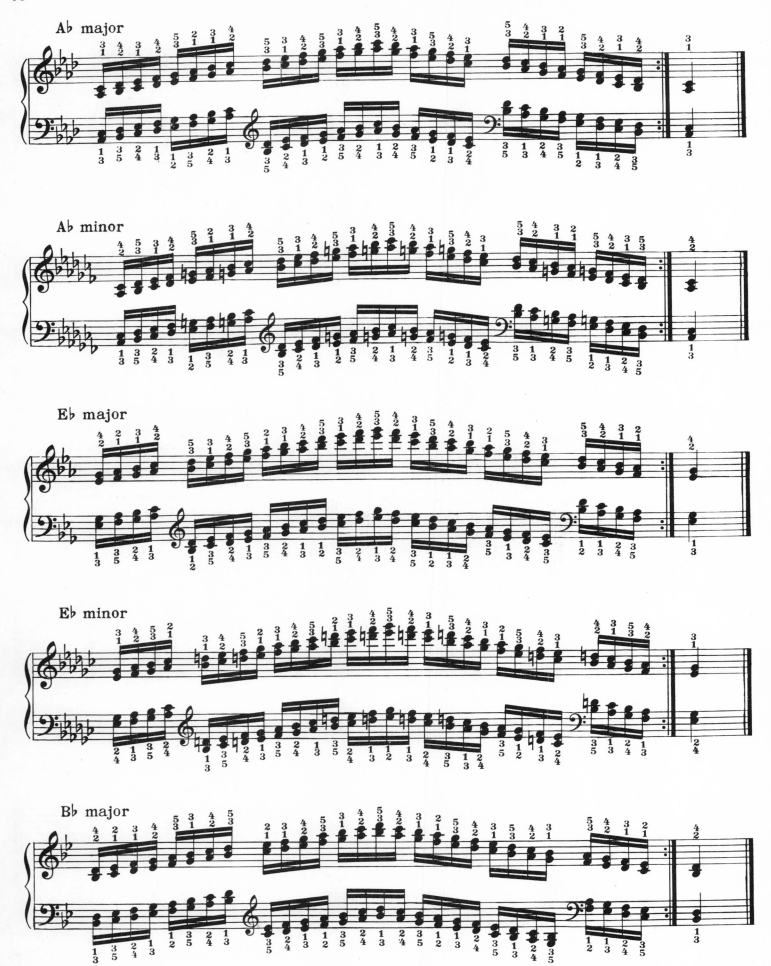

Ab major

Ab minor

Eb major

Eb minor

Bb major

B♭ minor

F major

F minor

Chromatic Scale in Double Minor Thirds

23a

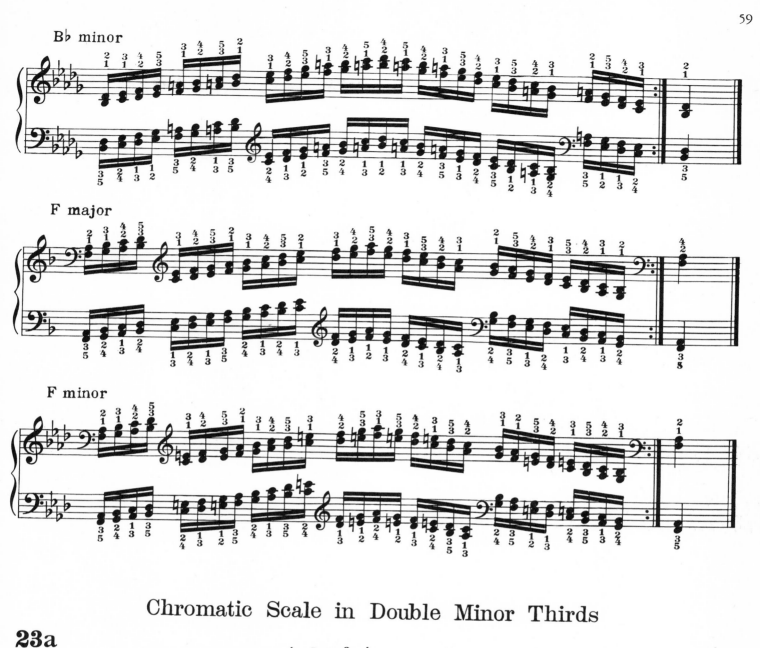

Right hand legato double-note figures

Carl Czerny

Left hand legato double-note figures

Carl Czerny

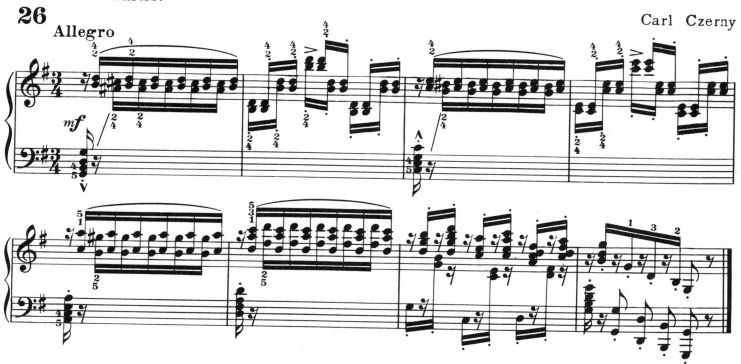

61

Play with sure, firm touch, rhythmic precision, and careful attention to the legato and staccato marks.

26

Carl Czerny

Allegro

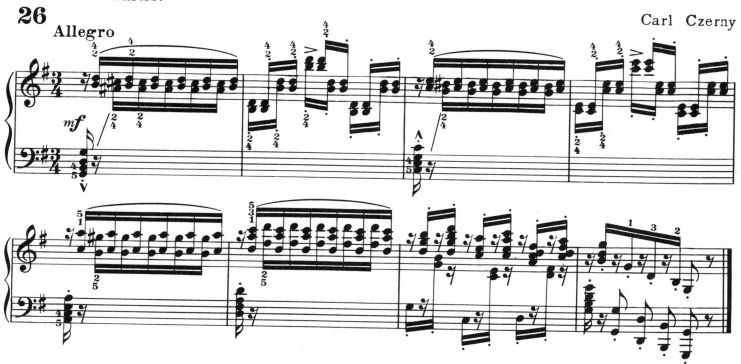

Contrary motion. Play firmly with exact rhythm.

27

Carl Czerny

Allegro

From GRADUS AD PARNASSUM

Play with a quiet hand and smooth minimal finger action. Vary the dynamics as you
wish. The goal is evenness, clarity, and speed.

28

Muzio Clementi

64

From GRADUS AD PARNASSUM

Play with a quiet hand and smooth, minimal finger action. Vary the dynamics as you wish.
The goal is evenness, clarity, and speed.

29

Muzio Clementi

From GRADUS AD PARNASSUM

Practice both legato and lightly detached.

30

Presto

Muzio Clementi

72

73

74

PRELUDE Op. 12, No. 7

The delicate brilliance of the right hand figures provide a shimmering contrast to the smoothly moving left hand melody

Serge Prokofieff

31 Vivo e delicato

Support the right hand melody with a smooth legato.

32

Carl Czerny

82

Staccato octaves with swift, relaxed wrist

Carl Czerny

33 Molto allegro

Staccato octaves with swift, relaxed wrist

Carl Czerny

34 Allegro

35

Molto allegro

Muzio Clementi

PRAELUDIUM

Polyphony in rapid tempo. Bring out all voices clearly.

Orlando Gibbons

36 Allegro moderato

88

Play with a light forearm and flexible wrist

37 Presto

Muzio Clementi

FUGUE (Three voices)

The fluency and steady, independent motion of the three voices should be maintained clearly throughout.

Johann Sebastian Bach

38

92

Use a sure, firm touch, sharp attack, and swift finger action.

39 Allegro con molto brio

Muzio Clementi

Staccato octave and chord passages; swift, relaxed wrist action

40

Muzio Clementi

Allegro vigoroso

GENERAL INDEX

Alberti bass   XI-33

Alternation between hands   X-17, X-22, X-101, X-102, X-103, X-105, X-106, X-127, X-134; XI-25, XI-40; XII-9, XII-45, XII-46, XII-47; XIII-11, XIII-13, XIII-16, XIII-19, XIII-26, XIII-34

Answering voices (CHARLES DENNÉE)   X-43, X-44

Arpeggiated triads   X-129, X-129a

Arpeggio studies   X-143 to X-146; XI-11, XI-12, XI-61; XII-19 to XII-23; XIII-12, XIII-13; *see also* Broken chords, Broken triads

Arpeggios
    dominant seventh   XII-41
    in all keys   XII-11, XII-18

BACH, JOHANN SEBASTIAN:
    Fugue   XIII-38
    Praeambulum in D minor   XII-15
    Praeambulum in B minor   XII-24

BEYER, FERDINAND: *Three Duets*   X-53, X-54, X-55

Broken chords   X-106, X-115; XI-13, XI-14, XI-28, XI-42, XI-63, XI-65, XI-66; XII-13, XII-37; XIII-2, XIII-3, XIII-4, XIII-31; *see also* Arpeggios; Broken triads; Divided chords

Broken intervals   X-35, X-36, X-37; XI-22; XII-12, XII-50, XII-54, XII-55

Broken octaves   XI-29; XII-53; XIII-16

Broken triads   X-95, X-96, X-100, X-102, X-105, X-121, X-125 to X-128; XI-26, XI-41

Canon   X-45, X-46, X-47

Cantabile   X-121, X-122; XI-23; XII-33

Change of fingers on one note   XI-27

Chords   X-111, X-119, X-120; XI-16, XI-74; XII-7, XII-10, XII-45, XII-47; XIII-8, XIII-37; *see also* Double notes; Repeated chords; Triads
    broken   X-106, X-115; XI-13, XI-14, XI-28, XI-42, XI-63, XI-65, XI-66; XII-13, XII-37; XIII-2, XIII-3, XIII-4, XIII-31
    divided   X-109, X-110, X-111, X-115

Chromatic scales
    at major sixth   XII-27
    at minor sixth   XII-28

Roman numerals (I, II, III, etc.) refer to Album Numbers

Arabic numerals (1, 2, 3, etc.) refer to Study Numbers

    at minor third   XII-26
    at octave   XII-25
    in double thirds   XIII-23

Chromatic studies   XI-38, XI-39, XI-59, XI-60; XII-29, XII-30

Contrary motion   X-57

CRAMER, LOUIS: *German Folk Song*   X-118

The Cuckoo (CHRISTIAN KOEHLER)   X-131

CZERNY, CARL: *Six Velocity Studies*   XI-17, XI-18, XI-19, XI-20, XI-21a, XI-21b

Damper pedal   XI-8, XI-26; XII-9, XII-14

DENNÉE, CHARLES:
    Answering Voices   X-43, X-44
    Three Little Canons   X-45, X-46, X-47

Divided chords   X-109, X-110, X-111, X-115

Dotted eighth notes   XI-10, XI-45, XI-52, XI-71

Dotted half notes   X-11

Dotted quarter notes   X-107, X-108, X-109

Double notes   X-65, X-66, X-116, X-117; XI-4, XI-50, XI-64, XI-70; XIII-9, XIII-11, XIII-21, XIII-22
    sixths   X-118, XI-15, XI-73
    thirds   X-58 to X-64, X-98, X-99; XI-72, XI-73; XII-34, XII-35, XII-40; XIII-14, XIII-24 to XIII-27, XIII-35

Duets   X53, X-54, X-55

Dynamics   X-13, X-14, X-15, X-26, X-44, X-48, X-49; XIII-1

Finger exercises   X-77, X-78, X-82 to X-88; XI-5

Finger staccato   X-18, X-19, X-42; XI-57; XII-4, XII-5

Five finger position   X-1 to X-21, X-23, X-24, X-26, X-28 to X-38, X-40, X-43 to X-51, X-53 to X-59, X-69 to X-73, X-75 to X-90, X-95, X-96, X-97, X-100
    shift of   X-25, X-27, X-42, X-52, X-74, X-98, X-99; XI-6
    with extensions   X-39, X-41, X-60 to X-68, X-91 to X-94

Forearm rotation   X-39, to X-42, X-100, X-121, X-126; XII-12, XII-63

Forearm staccato   XII-46, XII-53

German Folk Song (LOUIS CRAMER)   X-118

GIBBONS, ORLANDO: *Praeludium*   XIII-36

Glissandi   XIII-31

Grace notes   XI-23; XII-34, XII-35; XIII-25

High finger legato   X-17, X-74

HUMMEL, JOHANN: *Theme and Variations*   X-79

Imitation   X-24, X-43 to X-47, X-68

Independence of hands   X-28 to X-34, X-89, X-90

KABALEVSKY, DIMITRI:
   A Little Joke   XI-37
   Little Scherzo   X-42

KOEHLER, CHRISTIAN: *The Cuckoo*   X-131

Legato   *See* Cantabile; High Finger Legato

Legato and staccato   X-48, X-49, X-66, X-67, X-68, X-130, X-131; XI-36, XI-43, XI-49, XI-72; XII-46

Leger lines   X-69 to X-73

Leggiero   XI-35, XI-37, XI-55, XI-56; XII-54, XII-58, XII-59; XIII-7

A Little Joke (DMITRI KABALEVSKY)   XI-37

Little Scherzo (DMITRI KABALEVSKY)   X-42

Mordent   XI-51

MOUSSORGSKY, MODESTE: *Souvenir D'Enfance*   XIII-19

MÜLLER, A. E.: *Theme and Variations*   X-74

Non legato   X-79, X-116; XI-4

Octaves   XII-47, XII-48; XIII-27, XIII-33, XIII-34, XIII-40
  broken   XI-29; XII-53; XIII-16
  interlocking   XIII-16
  legato   XII-42, XII-43
  repeated   XII-56

Ornaments   *See* grace notes, mordent, trill, turn

Polyphony   XI-71, XII-8, XII-15, XII-16, XII-17, XII-31, XII-32; XIII-18, XIII-36, XIII-38

Praeambulum in D minor (JOHANN SEBASTIAN BACH)   XII-15

Praeambulum in B minor (JOHANN SEBASTIAN BACH)   XII-24

Praeludium (ORLANDO GIBBONS)   XIII-36

104

Prelude Op. 12, No. 7 (SERGE PROKOFIEFF)   XIII-31

Prelude No. 2 (DIMITRI SHOSTAKOVITCH)   XIII-7

PROKOFIEFF, SERGE: *Prelude Op. 12, No. 7*   XIII-31

Repeated chords
    legato   X-97, X-113; XI-68, XI-69
    staccato   X-112; XI-49, XI-64, XIII-17

Repeated notes
    with changing fingers   XI-48, XI-57, XI-58, XI-70; XII-10, XII-52
    with one finger   X-10, X-116; XI-9

Rhythm studies   X-80 to X-88; XI-53; XII-16
    dotted eighth notes   XI-10, XI-45, XI-52, XI-71
    dotted half notes   X-11
    dotted quarter notes   X-107, X-108, X-109
    six eight time   X-38
    syncopation   X-114, X-119; XI-7, XI-46

Scale studies   X-134, X-138 to X-142; XI-1, XI-2, XI-3, XI-24, XI-31, XI-32, XI-67;
        XII-2, XII-3, XII-6, XII-18; XIII-1, XIII-5

Scales
    in all keys   XII-1
    in double thirds   XIII-23
    major   X-136, X-137

Scales, Chromatic   *See* Chromatic scales

SHOSTAKOVITCH, DMITRI: *Prelude No. 2*   XIII-7

Six-eight time   X-38

Sixths   X-118; XI-15, XI-73

Slurs
    three note   X-48, X-60, X-61, X-65; XI-33, XI-47, XI-72
    two note   X-20, X-39, X-42, X-99, X-101; XI-33, XI-47, XI-67

Souvenir D'Enfance (MODESTE MOUSSORGSKY)   XIII-19

Staccato and legato   *See* Legato and staccato

Staccato
    finger   X-18, X-19, X-42; XI-57; XII-4, XII-5
    forearm   XII-46, XII-53
    wrist X-21, X-22, X-48, X-49, X-64, X-66, X-116, X-128; XI-15, XI-16, XI-29, XI-49,
        XI-50, XI-64, XI-72, XI-73; XII-7, XII-10, XII-44, XII-45, XII-47, XII-48, XII-
        56; XIII 40

Stretching exercises   XI-29, XI-30; XIII-6, XIII-15

Syncopation   X-114, X-119; XI-7, XI-46

Tenuto   X-19, X-22

Theme and Variations (Johann Hummel)   X-79

Theme and Variations (A. E. Müller)   X-74

Thirds   X-58 to X-64, X-98, X-99; XI-72, XI-73; XII-34, XII-35, XII-40; XIII-14, XIII-24 to XIII-27, XIII-35

Three Duets (Ferdinand Beyer)   X-53, X-54, X-55

Three Little Canons (Charles Dennée)   X-45, X-46, X-47

Thumb passing   X-135

Ties   X-12, X-23

Triads   X-91 to X-94; XI-54; XII-78 to XII-81
  arpeggiated   X-129, X-129a
  broken   X-95, X-96, X-100, X-102, X-105, X-121, X-125 to X-128; XI-26, XI-41
  repeated X-97; XII-44

Trills   X-75, X-76; XI-28, XI-52; XII-36 to XII-39, XII-49, XII-51

Triplets   X-62, X-123, X-124; XI-30

Turn   XI-8

Two against three   XII-61

Velocity studies   XI-3, XI-6, XI-17 to XI-20, XI-21a, XI-21b; XII-50, XII-54, XII-55, XII-57, XII-58, XII-59, XII-60, XII-62; XIII-1, XIII-3, XIII-5, XIII-8, XIII-10, XIII-12, XIII-13, XIII-20, XIII-28, XIII-29, XIII-30, XIII-32, XIII-39

Wrist staccato   X-21, X-33, X-48, X-49, X-64, X-66, X-116, X-128; XI-15, XI-16, XI-29, XI-49, XI-50, XI-64, XI-72, XI-73; XII-7, XII-10, XII-44, XII-45, XII-47, XII-56; XIII-40